CW00429078

BETHLEHEM TAILS

For concert use or as a musical play.

Music and words by Cyril Hambly
Storyline and Play by David Davies
Edited by Alison Hedger

For Junior and Lower Middle Schools.

Piano, vocal line and guitar chords.
Approximately 30 minutes of music.

The Christmas story as it may have been experienced by the animals at Bethlehem.

Introductory Music
1. Ox's Song
2. Cat's Song
3. Counsellors' Song
4. Camels' Song
5. Wise Men's Song
6. Donkey's Song
7. Joseph's Song
8. Shepherds' Song
9. Lamb's Song
10. Angels' Song
11. Animals' Lullaby
12. There are Tales

AN OPTIONAL NARRATION is included in this book -
for use in place of the play. This is best read by an adult.

Golden Apple Productions 1989
Hinton, Christchurch,
Dorset BH23 7EA
Telephone: (0425) 274993

ISBN 1 870997 15 8

© *Golden Apple Productions 1989 - "Bethlehem Tails"*

2

The play "Bethlehem Tails" is well within the scope of Junior and Middle School pupils. The play, together with the song words and vocal line choir parts is published separately - ISBN 1 870997 14 X - and copies can be obtained from Golden Apple Productions.

A cassette of the music is available from the publishers. Side 1 has the songs performed by Ferndown Middle School. Side 2 has the piano only and can be used for performances.

The division into solo and choir parts as given in the score, is optional. Any suitable allocation of parts which works well, is acceptable.

* * * * * * * * * * * * * *

INTRODUCTORY MUSIC

The introductory music can be used in its entirety at the beginning of a performance. The lights are raised at letter 'C' (onto area 1 if the play is being used), and the Narrator begins as the music concludes.

The introductory music may be used throughout when quiet music is required. Places to begin are indicated with letters, but any part of the music can be used with discretion, whenever the Narrator is speaking.

Narrator: Our tale begins one winter's night a long, long time ago, in an old tumble-down outhouse attached to a stable in Bethlehem. Inside the outhouse an old ox is recovering from a hard day's work. He is a lonely ox and wishes he had a friend.

© *Golden Apple Productions 1989 - "Bethlehem Tails"*

1. Ox's Song

© Golden Apple Productions 1989 - "Bethlehem Tails"

4

As the ox was thinking about his lonely life and all the work he had to do, a cat sidled into the outhouse. Oli asked her name and wondered where she had come from. "I'm Cleopatra - Cleo to my friends - I'm a royal cat from Herod's palace in Jerusalem" answered the cat. "If you like, I'll be your friend."

2. Cat's Song

Verse lyrics:

1) My name is Cle-o-pat-ra, I am a roy-al cat. I live at Her-od's pal-ace, and feed on this and that.
2) My name is Cle-o-pat-ra, I rub my roy-al fur a-gainst the pal-ace cush-ions and give a roy-al purr.
3) My name is Cle-o-pat-ra, I some-times take a nap u-pon a roy-al bed-spread or on a roy-al lap.

© Golden Apple Productions 1989 - "Bethlehem Tails"

Vocal line lyrics: When I am not sleep-ing, a care-ful watch I'm keep-ing to face them, and chase them, the roy - al mouse and rat.

Cleo told Oli how she had left Jerusalem because of Herod. Three visiting wise astrologers had come to the palace looking for a new king. Herod had gone into a mad rage and the whole palace had trembled at his stamping and show of temper. When the three astrologers had left to continue their search, Herod had thought of a devious and wicked plan - he asked the three men to return to him when they had found the new king and tell him of his whereabouts. Herod pretended that he too wanted to worship the new king, but really he wanted to kill the baby - leaving himself as the only king. Herod's counsellors had warned the wisemen of Herod's deceit.

© *Golden Apple Productions 1989 - "Bethlehem Tails"*

3. Counsellors' Song

© *Golden Apple Productions 1989 - "Bethlehem Tails"*

The ox was shocked at Herod's behaviour yet very interested in the cat's story. The animals' conversation was interrupted by a stable boy entering the outhouse leading three weary camels in need of food and rest. The cat recognized the camels "Why! here are Camilla, Calinda and Cassandra, the three camels camels who were carrying the three wise astrologers that I was just telling you about! I got away from Herod's unhappy palace hiding in Cassandra's back pack. Fancy us meeting up again in this old outhouse!"

© *Golden Apple Productions 1989 - "Bethlehem Tails"*

4. Camels' Song

1) I am a cam-el, and I am so proud of my hump; I am so proud of my
2) I am a cam-el, and up-on my back you may jump; up-on my back you ma[y]
3) I am a cam-el, when you ride me then you will bump; my lurch-ing steps make you[r]

hump-ty hump hump; my hump-ty hump, hump-ty hump, hump-ty hump hump; my hump-ty hump, hump-ty hum[p]
jump-ty jump jump; may jump-ty jump, jump-ty jump, jump-ty jump jump; may jump-ty jump, jump-ty jum[p]
bump-ty bump bump; you bump-ty bump, bump-ty bump, bump-ty bump bump; you bump-ty bump, bump-ty [bump]

hump.
jump.
bump.

SOLO

Cas-par ____ is my mas-ter, and he rode me ov-er the
Mel-chi-or ____ is my mas-ter, and he rode me ov-er the
Bal-tha-zar ____ is my mas-ter, and he rode me ov-er the

© *Golden Apple Productions 1989 - "Bethlehem Tails"*

© *Golden Apple Productions 1989 - "Bethlehem Tails"*

10

The three camels explained to Oli the ox that their masters, Caspar, Melchior and Balthazar, had been led to Bethlehem by understanding ancient writings and by the appearance of a new moving star which had stopped over the town. The camels told how special gifts of gold, frankincense and myrrh had been brought by their masters, and that they were now seeking the new King, so that they could present these gifts and pay Him homage.

5. Wise Men's Song

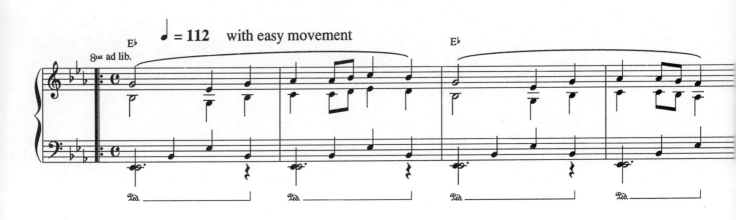

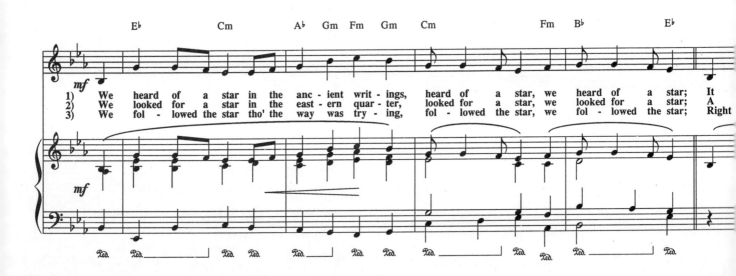

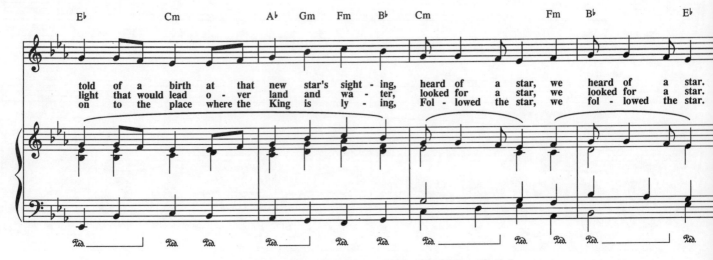

1) We heard of a star in the anc-ient writ-ings, heard of a star, we heard of a star; It
2) We looked for a star in the east-ern quar-ter, looked for a star, we looked for a star; A
3) We fol-lowed the star tho' the way was try-ing, fol-lowed the star, we fol-lowed the star; Right

told of a birth at that new star's sight-ing, heard of a star, we heard of a star.
light that would lead o-ver land and wa-ter, looked for a star, we looked for a star.
on to the place where the King is ly-ing, Fol-lowed the star, we fol-lowed the star.

© Golden Apple Productions 1989 - "Bethlehem Tails"

OIi was fascinated by the camels' story. All at once the outhouse door opened again and the stable boy led in a donkey."Hello, I'm Ned from Nazareth" said the donkey. "I've been led by my master and carried my mistress all the way here to Bethlehem in order that they could be included in the Roman census. It was a most difficult journey as I had to go so carefully - my mistress (Mary) is about to have a baby. And Joseph (my master) can't find anywhere for them to stay as the town is full up with all the other people fulfilling the census. Oh dear! I feel weary and wish that I could cheer things up for Joseph and Mary. If only I could carol and sing - instead of braying. How I would love to sing" said Ned.

© *Golden Apple Productions 1989 - "Bethlehem Tails"*

6. Donkey's Song

Lyrics:
1) E - yore, E - yore, ___ E - yore all day; noth - ing more pleas - ant, ___ have I to say.
2) No one, No one, ___ cares for my voice; it would be diff' - rent if I had a choice.
3) Ma - ry, Ma - ry, I car - ried to - day, gent - ly from Naz - a - reth, all of the way.

CHORUS: O how I wish I could car - ol and sing, mus - ic and danc - ing and pleas - ure I'd bring.

© *Golden Apple Productions 1989 - "Bethlehem Tails"*

The animals heard voices outside. The innkeeper, who owned the outhouse and stable, was telling someone that although this might be the tenth inn that they had tried, there simply just was no room for them in the inn here. However, as the travellers looked in real need, the innkeeper decided to let them rest in the stable alongside their donkey. "Why! it's Joseph and Mary" said Ned. The innkeeper led the couple through the outhouse into the stable. Joseph moved Ned over and shut the stable door. He made a comfortable place in the straw for Mary to rest.

7. Joseph's Song

© *Golden Apple Productions 1989 - "Bethlehem Tails"*

All was quiet inside the outhouse, when singing was heard - in the distance at first - then nearer and nearer it came.

8. Shepherds' Song

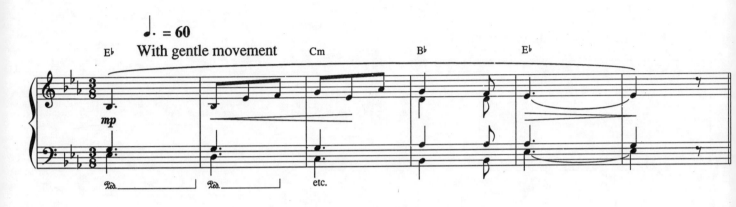

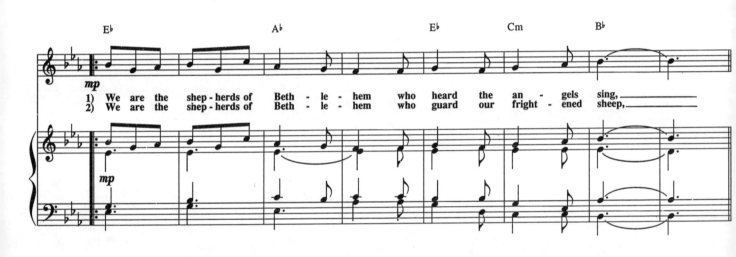

1) We are the shep-herds of Beth - le - hem who heard the an - gels sing,_____
2) We are the shep-herds of Beth - le - hem who guard our fright - ened sheep,_____

We are the shep-herds of Beth - le - hem, who go to see the King._____
We are the shep-herds of Beth - le - hem, a care - ful watch, we keep._____

© *Golden Apple Productions 1989 - "Bethlehem Tails"*

Out on the hill; qui - et and still; the sheep are safe from harm. _____

While we are near, noth - ing to fear ever - y one is calm. _____

A group of shepherds came into the outhouse. They were talking in soft voices to the stable boy, telling him what had just happened out on the hillside, whilst they were tending their sheep. An angel had appeared and told them to go down into Bethlehem and look for a special baby lying in a manger. The stable boy told the shepherds that the lady who was asleep in his stable was about to have a baby, so perhaps they had come to the right place! The stable boy picked up one of the shepherd's little lambs and cuddled him - his woolly coat was warm and soft.

© *Golden Apple Productions 1989 - "Bethlehem Tails"*

9. Lamb's Song

© *Golden Apple Productions 1989 - "Bethlehem Tails"*

leap from the ground, an e - nor - mous height and make such a boun - cy, hap - py sight.
I have a warm and cud - dly coat and cry with such a touch - ing note.
try not to let my wor - ries show but far from the shep - herd I'll not go.

Baa - baa, ba ba ba ba baa.
Baa - baa, ba ba ba ba baa.
Baa - baa, ba ba ba ba

CODA

(both voices)

baa.

Baa - baa, ba ba ba ba

baa.

subito *p*

sempre *f*

8va basso

© *Golden Apple Productions 1989 - "Bethlehem Tails"*

Outside in the night air a different song could be heard. "The sky is full of angels singing - what a wonder!" marvelled the shepherds.

© *Golden Apple Productions 1989 - "Bethlehem Tails"*

10. Angels' Song

2) Blow, all the trumpets blow;
Let the whole wide world be knowing.
Blow, all the trumpets blow,
    For the birth of Jesus.

3) Strum, all the harp-strings strum;
For the news that he is coming.
Strum, all the harp-strings strum,
    For the birth of Jesus.

4) Clish, clash, the cymbals clash;
Golden cymbals gaily flashing.
Clish, clash the cymbals clash,
    For the birth of Jesus.

5) Ring, all the church-bells ring;
All the joys of Christmas bringing.
Ring, all the church-bells ring,
    For the birth of Jesus.

© *Golden Apple Productions 1989 - "Bethlehem Tails"*

20

The ox, cat, camels and Ned pricked up their ears at the angels' singing. Oli asked a little lamb to go and take a peek inside the stable. This he willingly did and returned with his face shining. "Hush all you animals. The baby has been born and lies in the manger. His mother is resting and Joseph is looking after them."

11. Animals' Lullaby

© Golden Apple Productions 1989 - "Bethlehem Tails"

© *Golden Apple Productions 1989 - "Bethlehem Tails"*

22

All the animals were filled with a nice warm feeling. "There Oli" said the cat. "Now you have many friends - and what a tale all the animals can tell of tonight's goings on!" "A tale" said Oli - "A T-A-L-E isn't the only tail we animals have. What about our T-A-I-L-S ?? Bethlehem tails !!" All the animals laughed and the cat twirled her tail.........................

12. There are Tales

© Golden Apple Productions 1989 - "Bethlehem Tails"

© *Golden Apple Productions 1989 - "Bethlehem Tails"*

The story we have just told recounts the birth of Jesus Christ - that very special baby born long ago - who cam
to earth to bring peace and love to everyone. So now we wish you and all those you love, a very happy
Christmastime.   (Optional repeat of song 11 - Animals' Lullaby)   * THE END *

© Golden Apple Productions 1989 - "Bethlehem Tails"